Draw Your World

3/6

This edition published by Parragon Books Ltd in 2014

Parragon Books Ltd
Chartist House
15–17 Trim Street
Bath BA1 1HA, UK
www.parragon.com

Written by Frances Prior-Reeves
Designed by Talking Design
Illustrations by Carol Seatory

ISBN 978-1-4723-7742-5

Printed in China

Draw Your World

PaRragon

Bath · New York · Cologne · Melbourne · Delhi
Hong Kong · Shenzhen · Singapore · Amsterdam

Draw an animal
CURLED UP
in front of a fire.

Fill this page with LEAVES.

**Can you transform those leaves
into a pack of**

WOLVES?

Draw the

characters

of a story.

Space for
your ideas.

Turn these shapes into
ghosts.

Imagine,
then draw!

Draw what is under the BED.

Draw...

a *witch*,

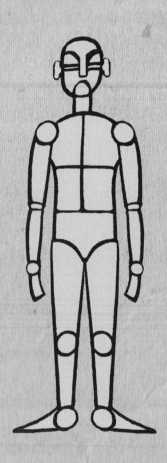

an ANDROID

and an

ESCAPE ARTIST.

Now draw one image of all three.

Fill this bug tank with INSECTS.

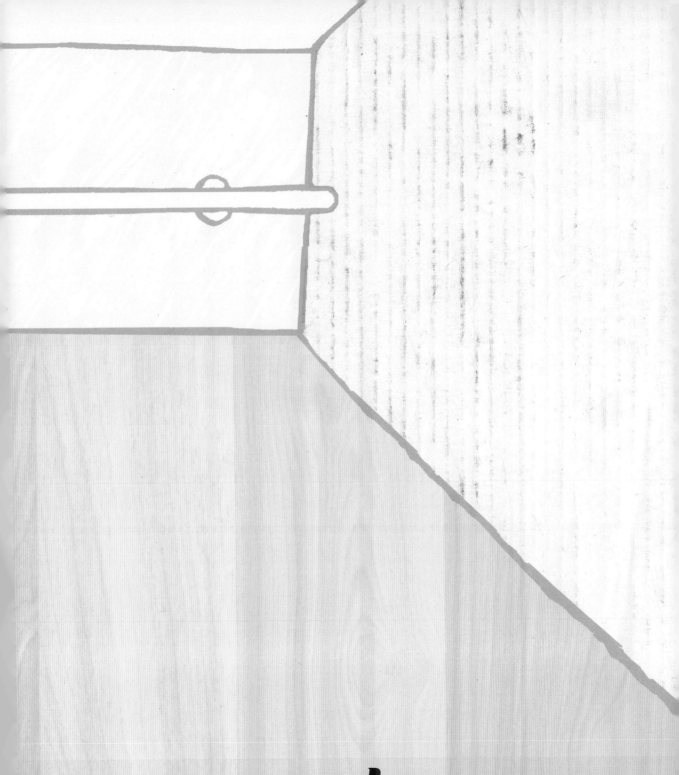

Add *dancers* to this performance space.

Fill this MATCHBOX

with as many tiny objects as you can.

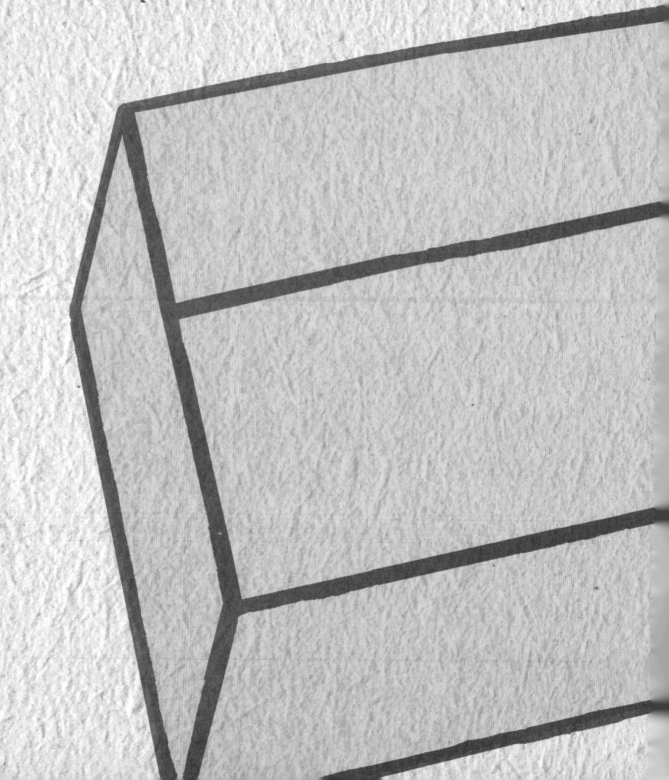

Create a MOSAIC

of an important leader.

Practice on the larger grid and then refine your design.

Fill this jar with

screws.

Draw something lazy.

Draw something

hyperactive.

Personalize
these pages.

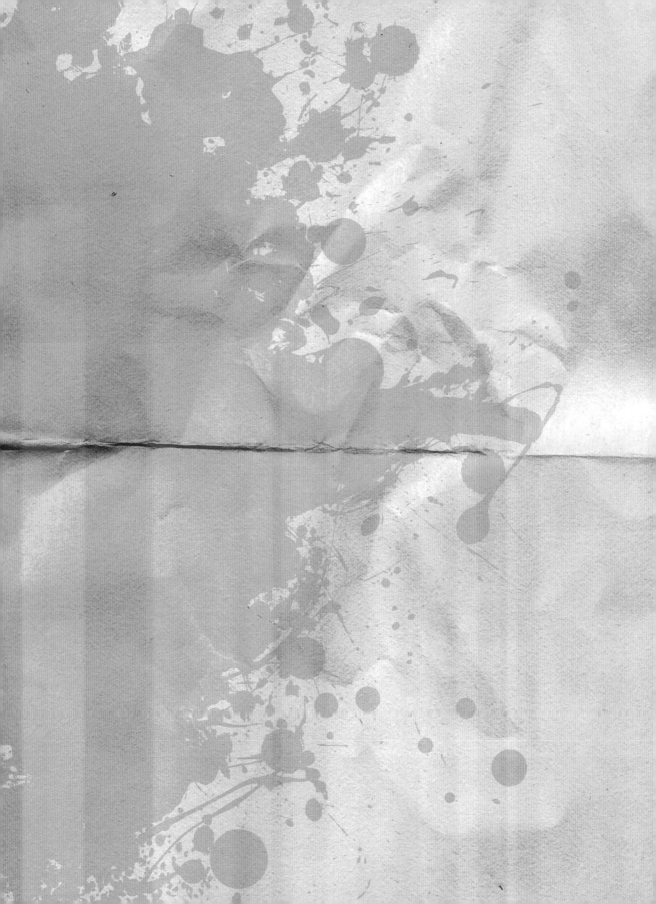

Fill these bowls with
CRISPS
and DIPS.

Draw a famous LANDMARK.

Add **faces** to these noses.

Draw what this seal is
juggling.

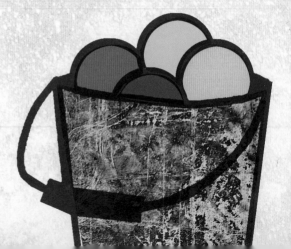

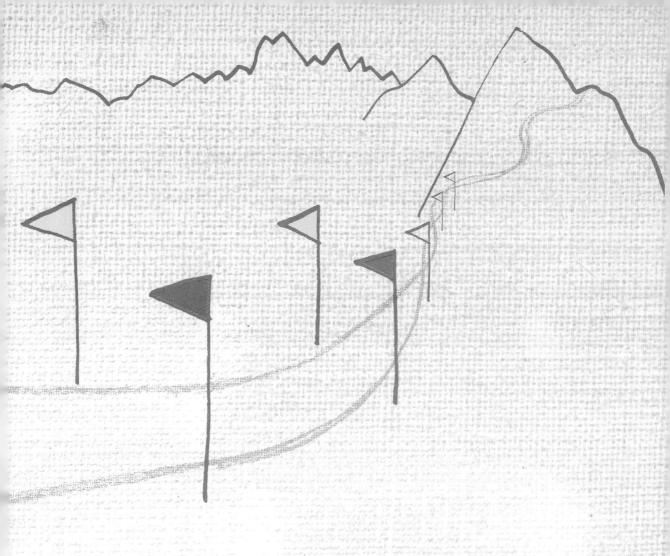

Add a skier **to this slalom run.**

Add some **ART** to these frames.

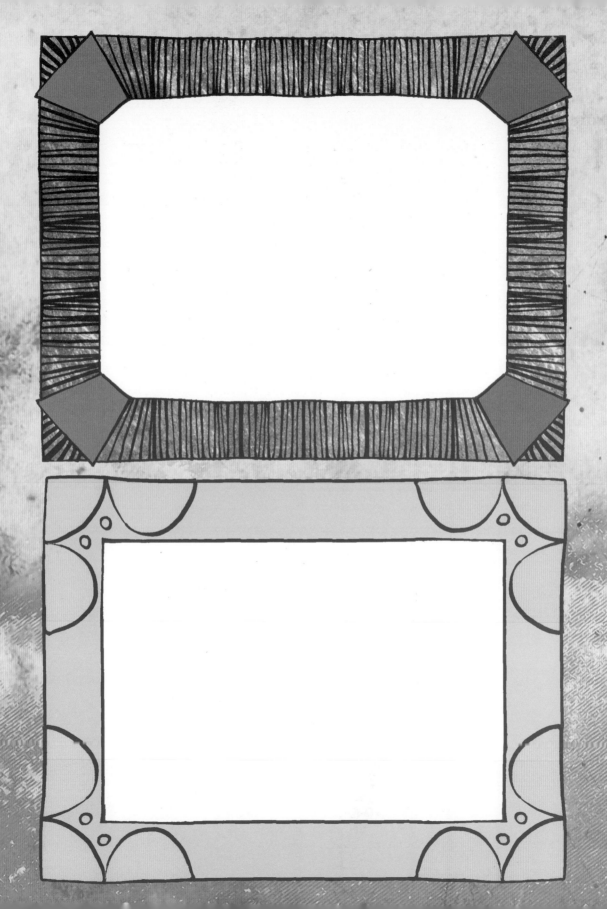

Draw your **dream.**

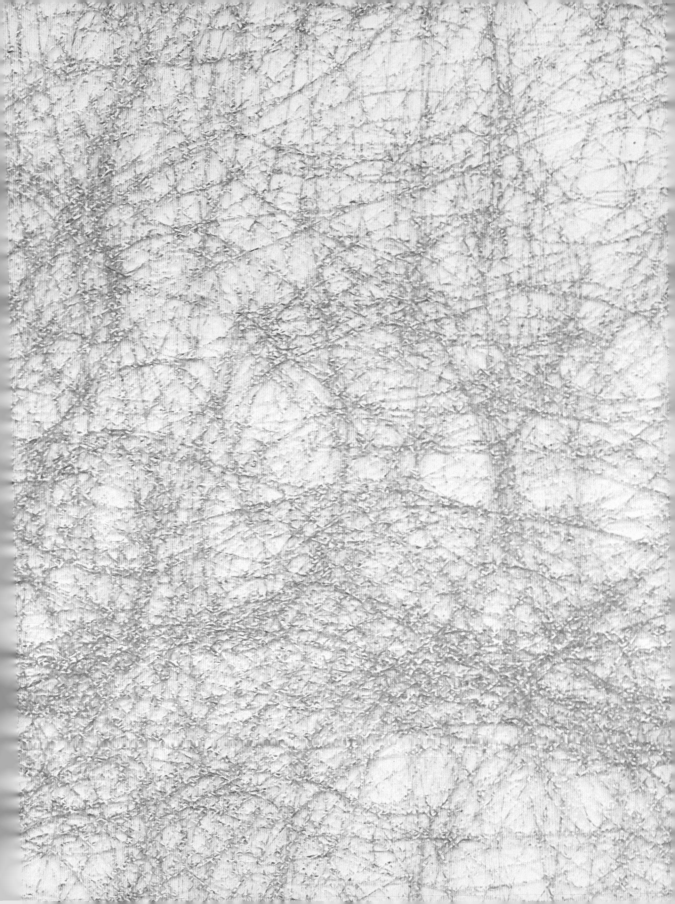

Fill this swimming pool with
slides, floats
and swimmers.

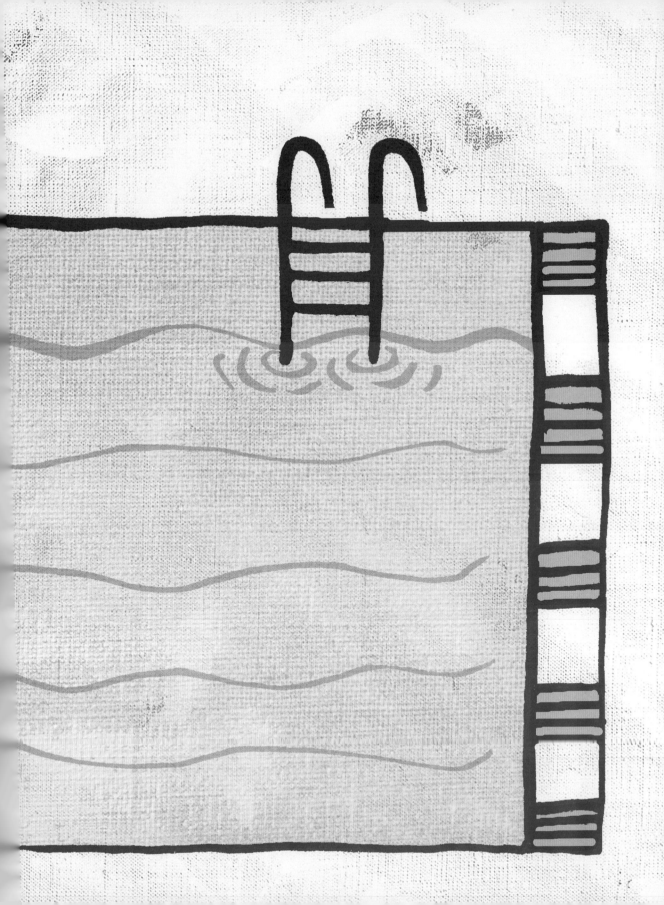

Draw a boat that can **Fly**.

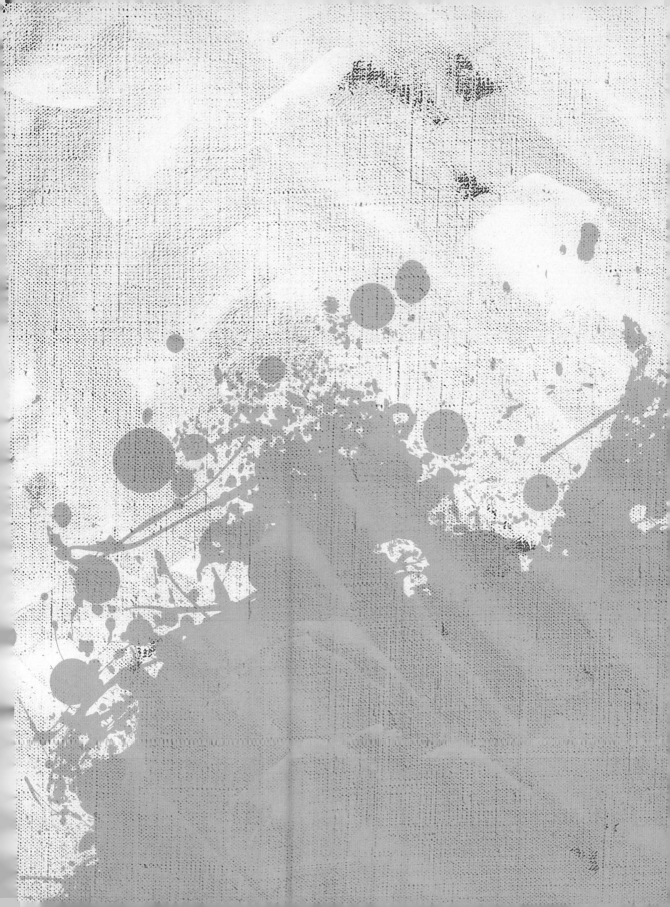

Draw half of a **LION'S**
FACE on one side
of this circle ...

... and draw half of a

TIGER'S
FACE

on the other side.

Add
TATTOOS
to these arms.

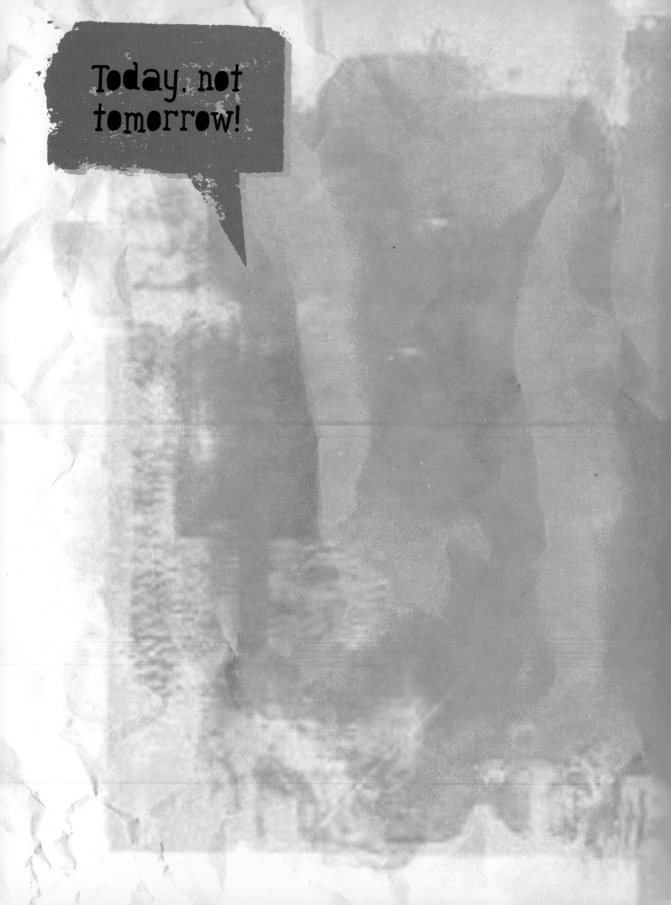

Today, not tomorrow!

Draw what is above ...

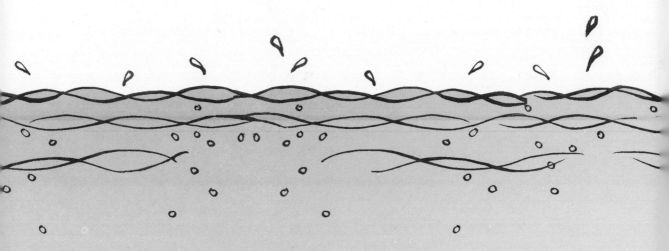

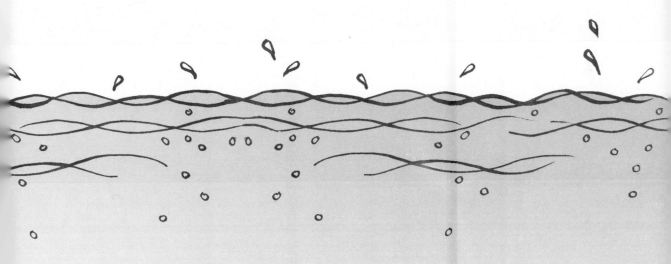

and **below** this waterline.

Design these
TIES.

Add jewellery

to this shop display.

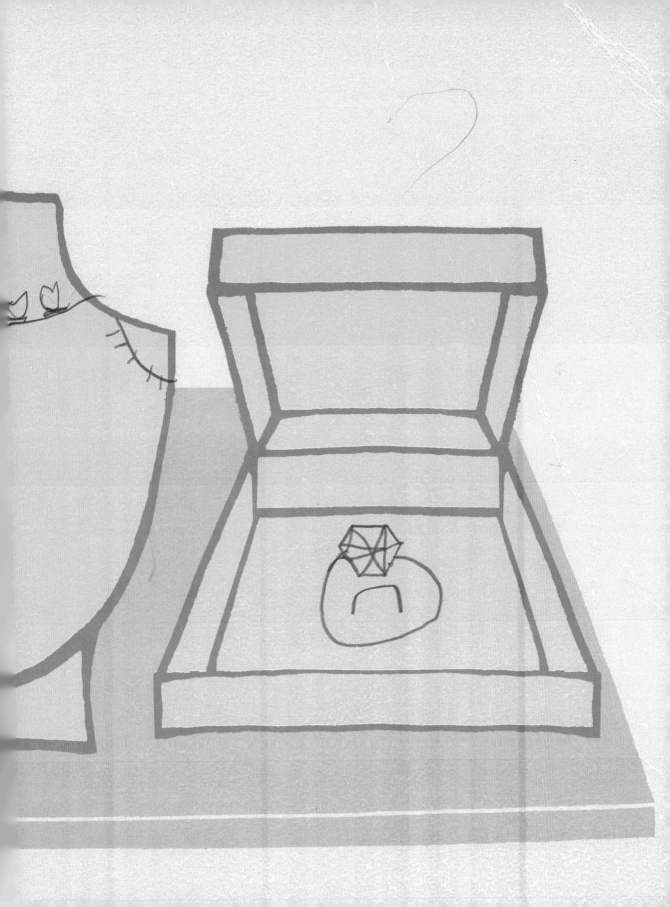

Fill this page with CIRCLES.

Can you transform those circles into a celebrity?

Dress these
CLOWNS.

Fill these jars with

pens, paper clips, & elastic bands.

bulldog clips,

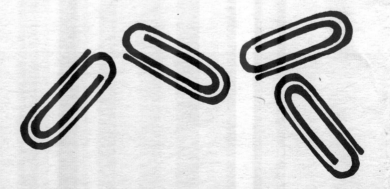

Add toppings to these baps to create two delicious
BURGERS.

Draw ALIENS on their home planet.

Add **wings** to this bird.

Pick up
a pencil.

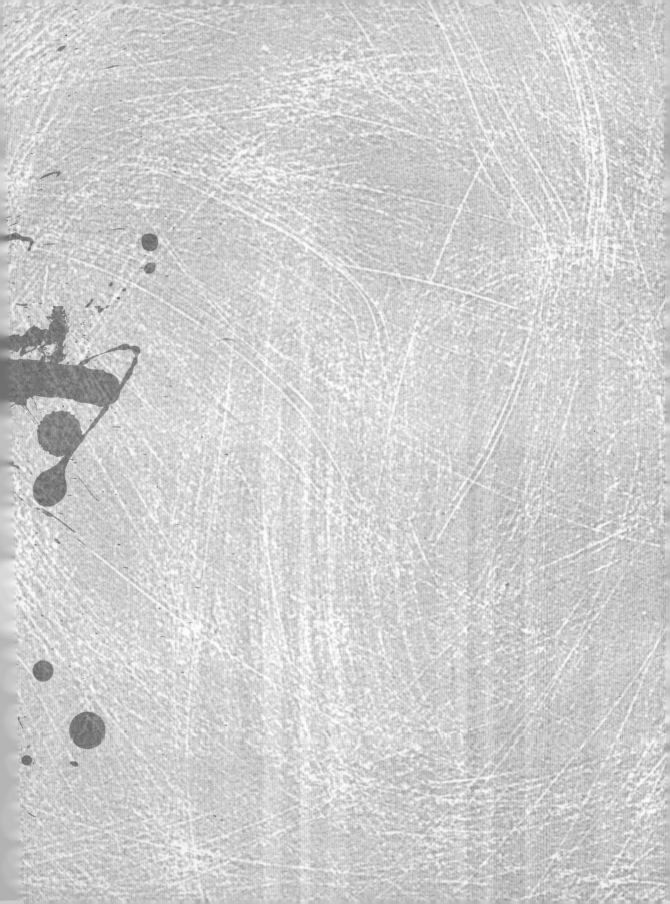

Design a
UNIFORM
for your favourite sports team.

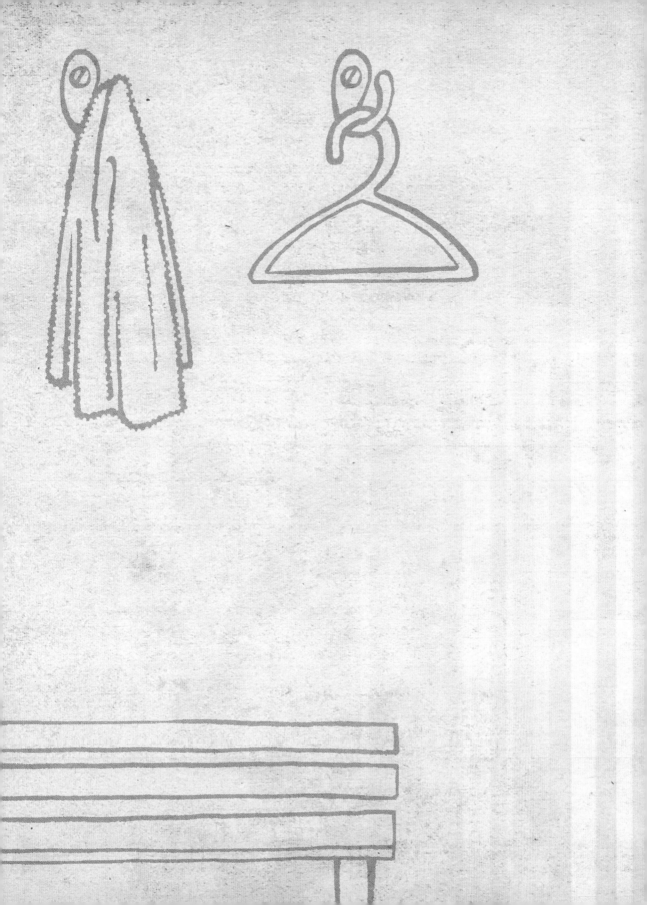

Fill this forest with

LIFE.

Space to do anything.

Draw your favourite pair of
SHOES.

Draw your
GYM SHOES.

Draw a
SKYdiver

jumping from this aeroplane.

Shade
something!

Draw the contents of this

HANDBAG.

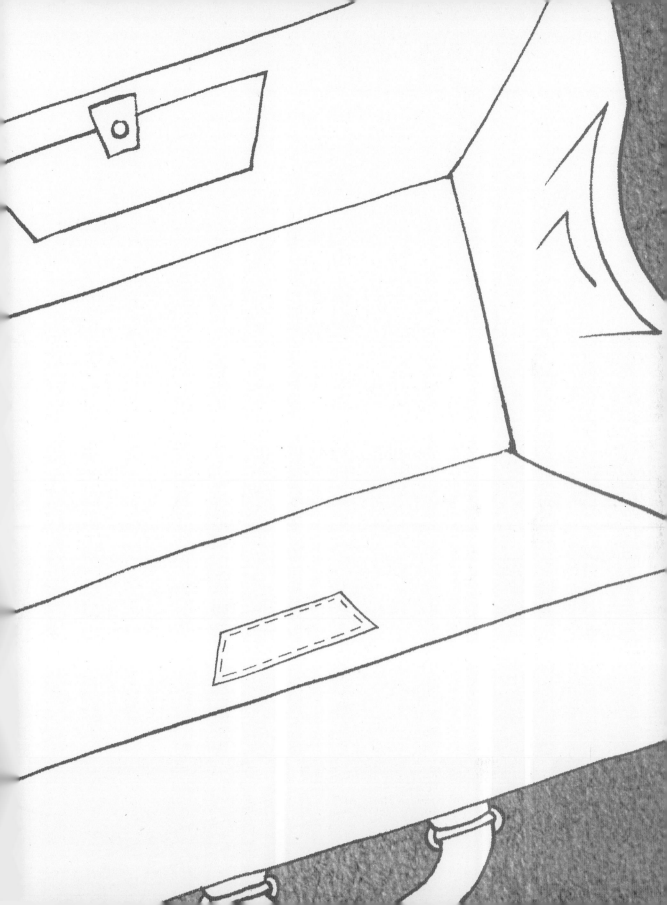

Design a BUILDING
using this graph paper.

Draw a **Shark** chasing its prey.

Draw what is
COOKING
on this hob.

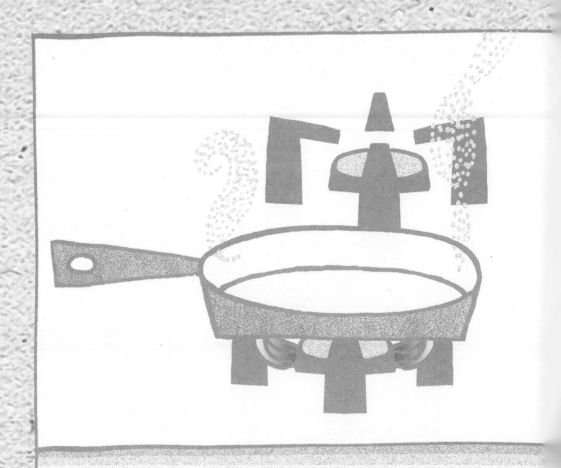

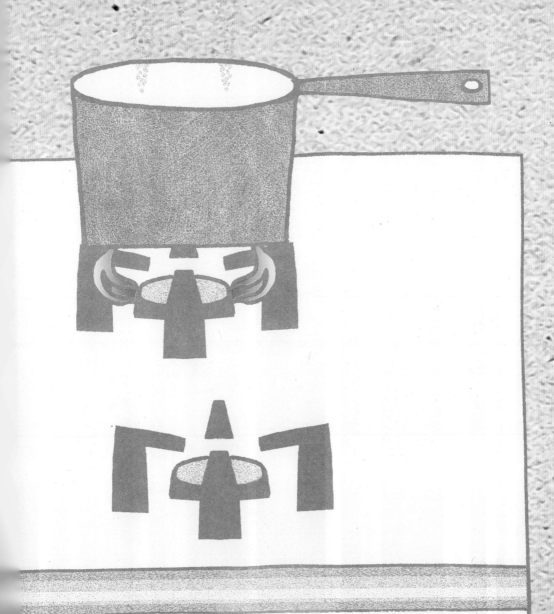

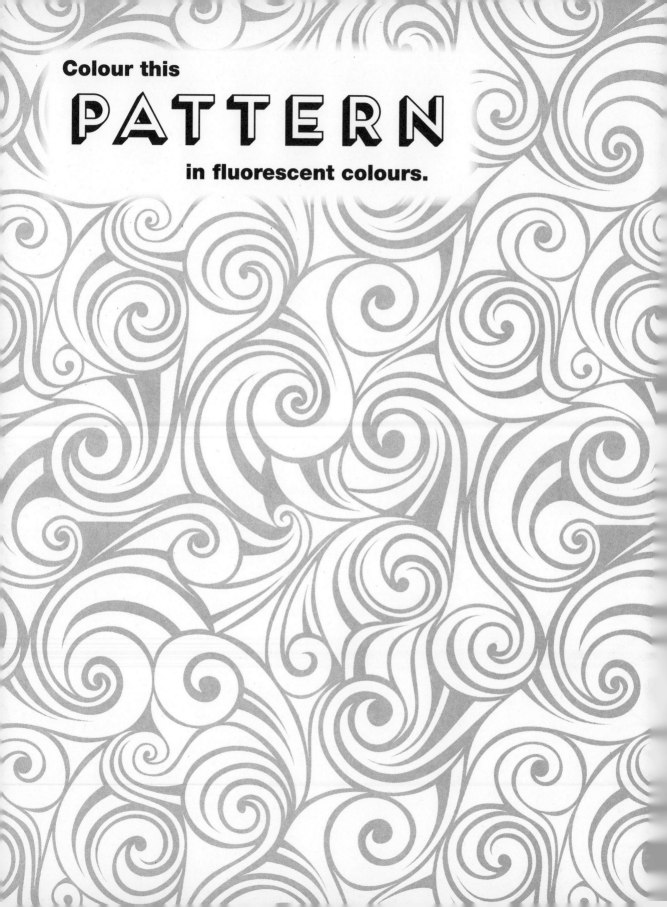

Colour this
PATTERN
in fluorescent colours.

Fill this bookshelf with
books.

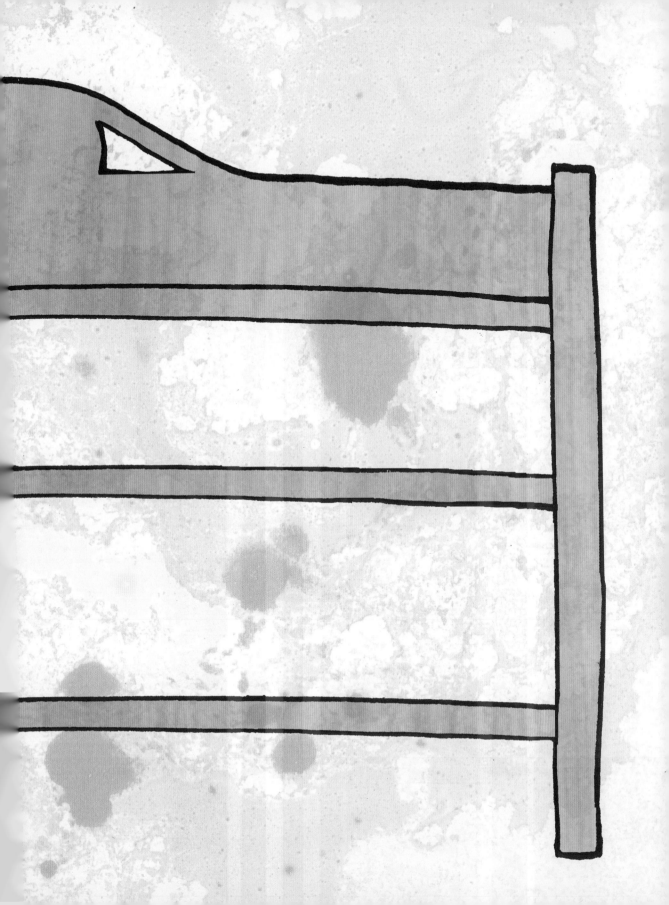

Draw half of a

chameleon's
face on one side

of this circle ...

... and draw
half of an

**owl's
face**

on the other
side.

Add passengers to this
rowing boat.

Scribble something!

Turn these shapes into
caterpillars.

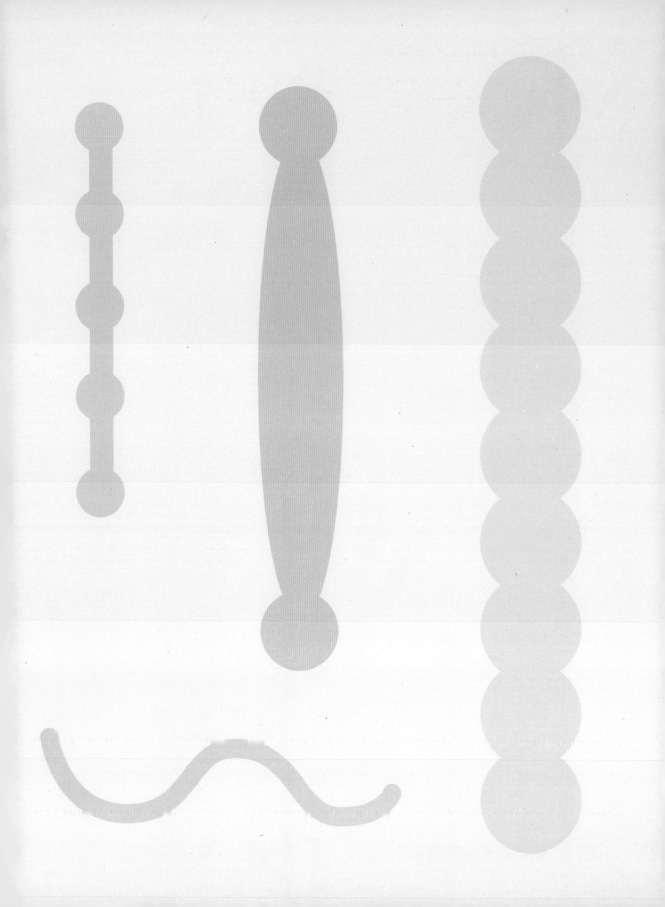

Fill these pots with **plants**.

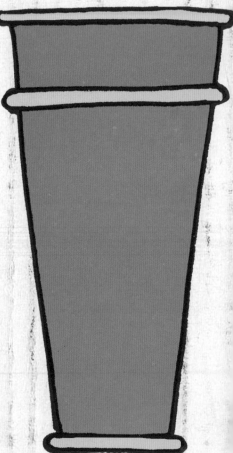

Draw a  **chasing this ball.**

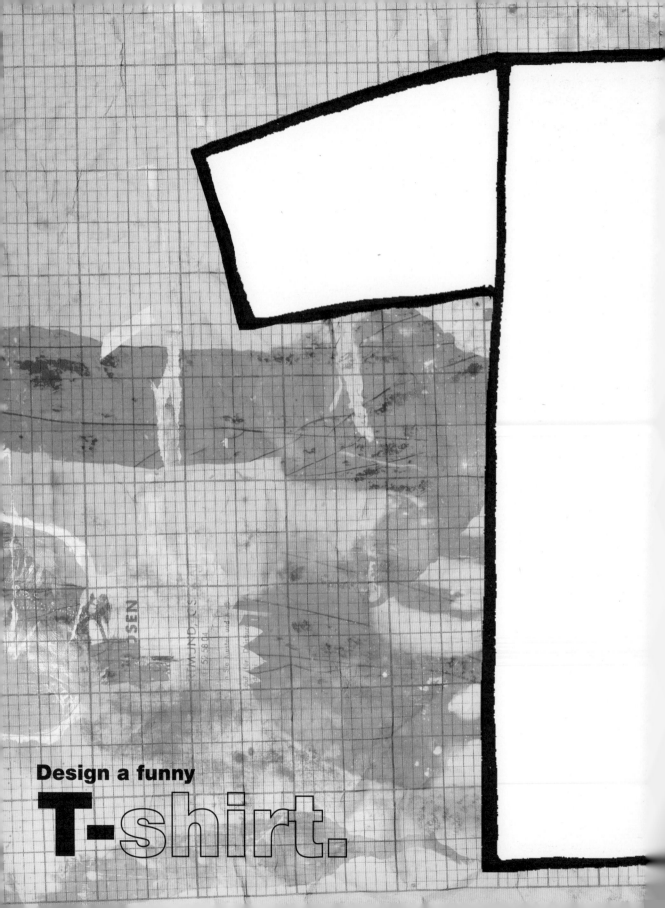

Design a funny
T-shirt.

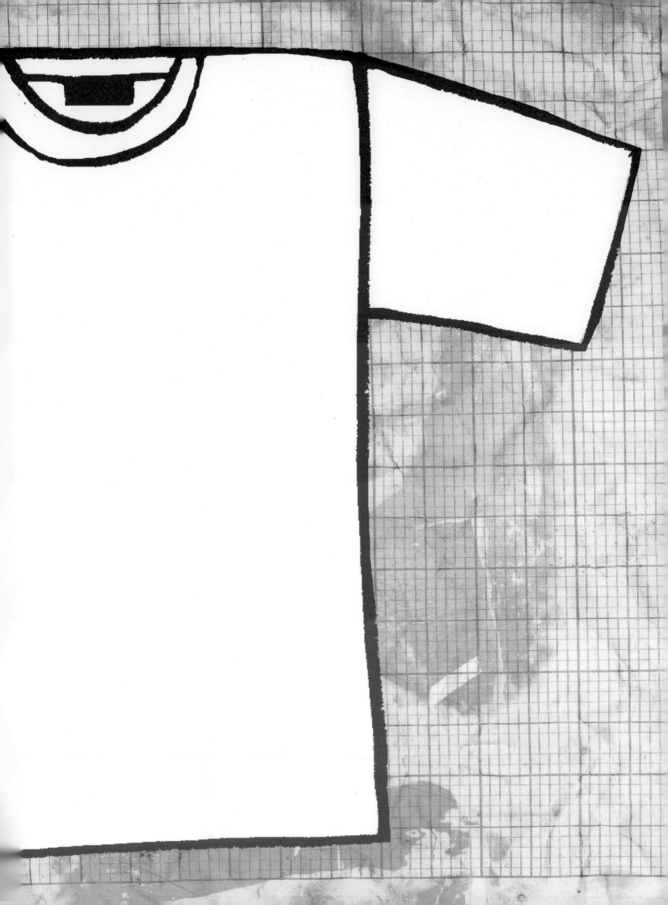

Draw ...

a RHINOCEROS,

a MEERKAT

and a **GIRAFFE.**

Now draw one image of all three.

Design a flag for a new nation.

Fill this jar with
toy soldiers.

There are
no limits!

Draw the other half of this

AEROPLANE.

Add faces to these
moustaches.

Fill this page with

DIAGONAL
LINES.

Can you transform
   those lines into a reptile?

Draw yourself as a
FEMALE
on this page.

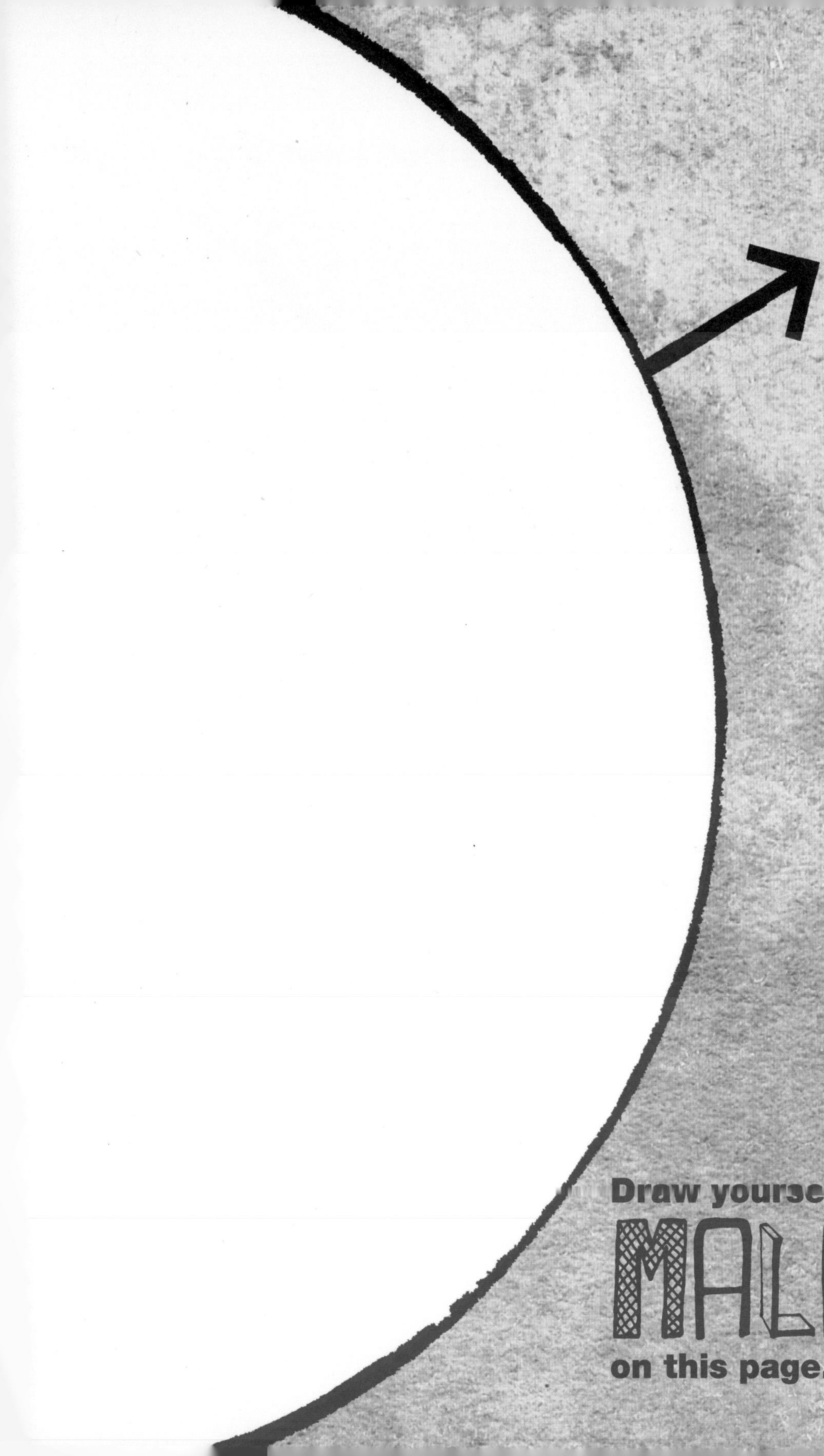

Draw yourself as a

MALE

on this page.

Add some fruit to this fruit bowl.

Fill this snow scene with

Add clothes to these

mannequins.

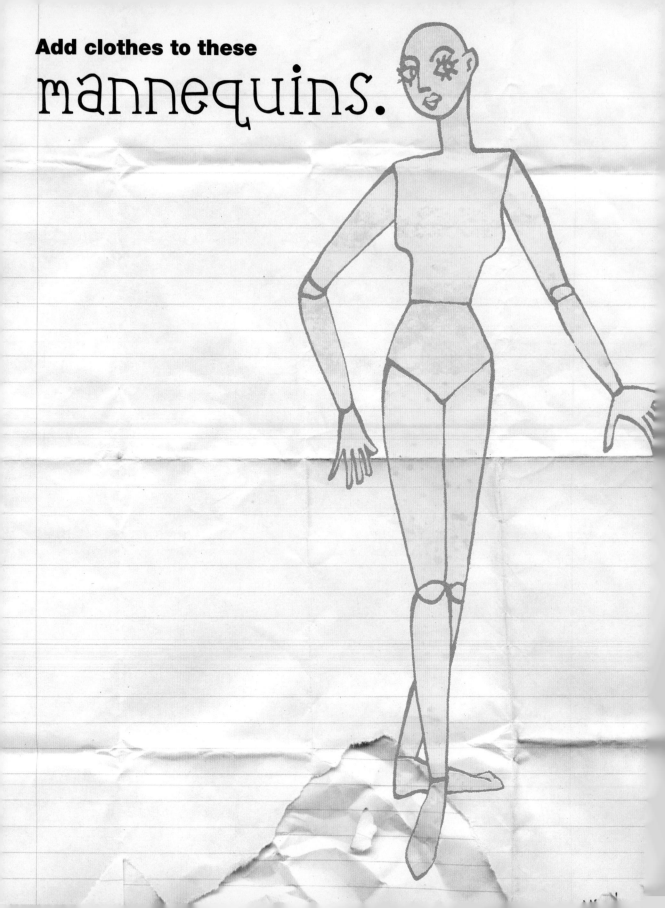

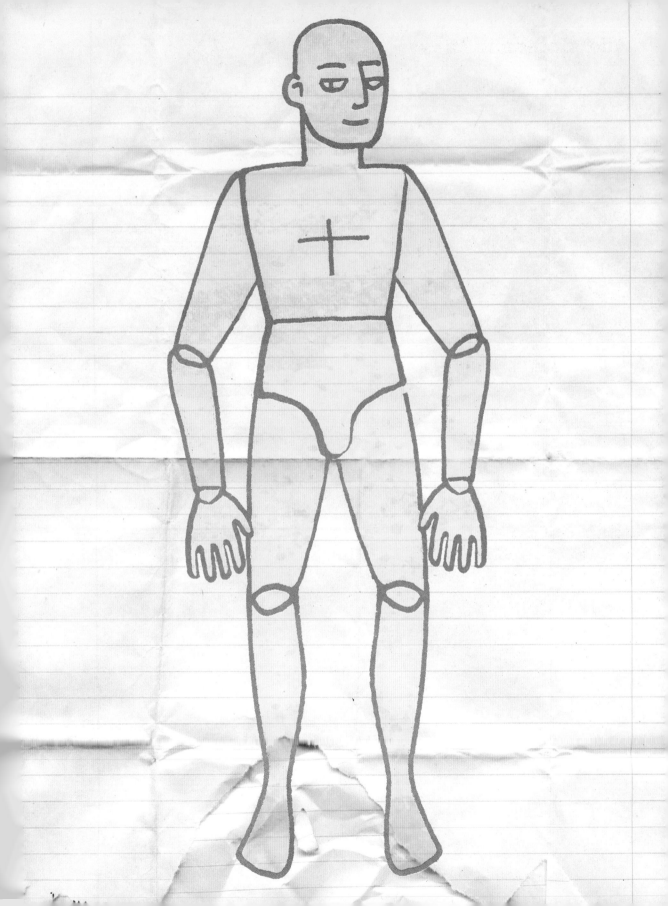

Create art.

Draw SPIDERWEBS

glistening in the dark.

Draw an **elephant** in a tiny hat.

Draw a **flamingo** in a giant hat.

Draw something coming down these stairs.